Dedicated to those that sometimes maybe wish they were a bit more like everyone else. Please know that you are already perfect as you are. You dance, play, sing and learn in your own unique and wonderful way.

You're a unicorn, uniquely rare!
Your beauty is beyond compare.
You're special from the day you're born,
You really are a unicorn!

This book belongs to

_____

For there is no one quite like you!

I'm Basically A

WRITTEN AND ILLUSTRATED BY
MELANIE HAWKINS

Unicorn

Inspire Joy
Publishing, LLC

My eyes are blue, my hair is red,
And curly right upon my head.
My traits are so unique and rare,
There's no one like me anywhere.

A unicorn's uniquely rare
With beauty that's beyond compare.
I have been me since I was born.
I'm basically a unicorn!

My wheelchair helps me get around,
And often I don't make a sound.
I'm very good at hide and seek,
But I love most that I'm unique!

A unicorn's uniquely rare.
With wheels I move in my
own chair.
A unicorn sure likes to play
With friends that I see
everyday.

I have a pump, but some may not.
My glucose count gets checked a lot.
A book's adventure is so neat.
Reading is my favorite treat!

A unicorn's uniquely rare,
Sometimes needing extra care.
In books new friends I love to meet.
I'm smart and brave, so strong and
sweet.

The world's unique in my own mind.
A view like mine is hard to find.
My brain is different from the rest,
But being different is the best!

A unicorn's uniquely rare.
We love to swing high in the air.
I am a unicorn like you,
And play is what we like to do!

Chemo made me lose my hair.
No wigs for me 'cause I don't care!
No fancy hat upon my head,
I'd rather jump my rope instead.

A unicorn's uniquely rare
With beauty that's beyond compare.
In me a unicorn you'll find.
I'm fierce and tough,
so brave and kind!

As twins we have the same kind heart,
Same hair and eyes right from the start.
We're both alike but different, too.
I'm just like me; you're just like you.

A unicorn's uniquely rare.
No two the same; you can't compare.
No one's like me or just like you.
We are both unicorns, it's true!

U-N-I-Q-U-E

The way I look sets me apart.
In glasses I feel super smart.
First place! I won the Spelling Bee!
I am so very proud of me!

S-P-E-C-I-A-L

A unicorn's uniquely rare
With talents that we love to share.
A unicorn is smart, it's true.
It looks like me and just like you.

Extra chromosome, extra love,
Sent so perfect from above.
I'm Down right good at what I do.
I'll make you smile and love you, too!

A unicorn's uniquely rare.
Our joy for life we love to share.
My smile's brightly on my face.
I make our world a better place!

Maybe I am very tall.
Maybe I am very small.
It makes no difference, can't you see?
I'm just the perfect size for me!

A unicorn's uniquely rare.
The size of me you can't compare.
I am the perfect fit for me,
Exactly how I'm meant to be!

I don't see as others do.
I've learned new ways to help me through.
There's beauty all around for me.
I touch, taste, hear, and smell to see.

A unicorn's uniquely rare.
It's how we see the world we share.
Though much the same for you and me,
Mine has beauty you can't see!

Swimming is the very best.
Underwater, I feel blessed.
No other place I'd rather be,
A mermaid unicorn like me!

We're unicorns, both me and you,
Doing what we love to do.
But no one else is quite like me,
Uniquely special as can be.

Our challenges are great and small.
Highs or lows—embrace them all!
Uniqueness gives us priceless worth.
We spread our rainbow
through the earth.

We are each uniquely rare
With beauty that's beyond compare.
There's no one that's
like me or you.
We all are unicorns,
it's true!

What makes us unique and special:
trait (noun)\ trāt

A distinguishing quality/an inherited characteristic

We may feel that looking different or being different is hard. But in reality, no two people on the earth are exactly the same. Our uniqueness in features, personality, preferences, traits, and abilities is what makes us so special.

 Did you know that red hair and blue eyes is the most genetically rare hair and eye color combination in the world? Only 17% of the population have blue eyes, and 2% have red hair! Pretty cool, right?

 There are lots of reasons someone may be in a wheelchair. Paralysis, health conditions that affect one's ability to walk, surgery, or a broken bone—just to name a few. Did you know that there are sports especially for wheelchair-bound people? There are even races and Olympic Games!

Diabetes affects the body's ability to produce insulin, a necessary factor in helping the body break down and absorb sugar. People with diabetes have to check their blood sugar count often and follow a strict diet. Sometimes they check it with a little drop of blood from a finger prick and sometimes from a device implanted on their body that can track it. It is vital to keep their numbers in check.

There are many reasons why some people's brains work differently. This can make doing new things or processing information very difficult for some people. Did you know that some of the most brilliant people in the world had trouble with very basic things? Albert Einstein's teachers were unsure of him as a student, but his mother understood that he just had a different learning style, and taught and encouraged his curiosity.

Cancer is a disease that often requires medication that can cause hair loss in young people. There are also other conditions such as alopecia that can cause hair loss. None of these are contagious and are not anyone's fault. Of course hair loss for older people is much more common.

Identical twins look alike and sometimes have many more similarities. There are some types of twins called fraternal twins that may look quite different. They might even be different genders. No matter how similar they may seem, each person has their own unique qualities and preferences and personalities. They are each unique.

Our skin is our largest organ and protects the insides of our body. Skin comes in lots of different colors with numerous shades. It can have distinguishing marks like freckles or birthmarks and can even have other conditions such as vitiligo. Vitiligo affects the immune system which then affects the skin, resulting in white patches. It is not contagious and there is no known cure. Did you know that there are 70 million people with this condition, including a famous model?

We all have chromosomes that make us unique. People with Down syndrome are born with an extra chromosome that alters their development and may cause distinguishing characteristics. They can have varying forms of cognitive disability. If you get to know someone with Down syndrome, you will find that they have unique personalities and interests, just like everyone else! They can play sports, create art, play instruments, and want to have fun and make new friends like all kids do.

Our height is something that can make us really stand out in a crowd or feel like we don't quite measure up. It can be hard to be on either extreme. Often it is genetic and there is usually nothing we can do about it. So embrace your size exactly as you are. Fun fact: Girls usually reach adult height by age 14–16 and boys by age 16–18.

When someone is blind, it means that they cannot see. They might not be able to see at all or just not very clearly. They may be able to see unfocused shapes or colors. People can become blind because of diseases or accidents, but sometimes people are born blind. When people are blind they use their other senses to do the things their eyes would normally do. They can read using the alphabet in braille and might use special animals like guide dogs to do everyday things.

Sometimes people are born without a limb, but sometimes it is the result of an injury or illness. Prosthetics are a type of artificial limb that can be used as a child gets older, or they might use a splint or brace to help do things that other children do. Did you know that there are people with limb differences that are world class athletes, dancers, pilots, musicians, models, actors, and politicians? They can do most everything anyone else can do.

Inspire Joy Publishing, LLC
Thank you to my book formatter Praise Saflor and to my amazing editor (who loves her anonymity)! Thank you!

Paperback edition
ISBN 978-1-7341650-6-7
Library of Congress Control
Number: 2020901988

Inspire Joy Publishing can provide special discounts when purchased in larger volumes for premiums and Promotional purposes, as well as for fundraising and educational use.

Inspire Joy
Publishing, LLC

Meet the Author & Illustrator

Author and illustrator Melanie Hawkins was born and raised in the United States in a charming little farming town in Idaho, but has made her home in the beautiful state of Utah. She and her wonderful husband have 7 amazing children. Her family is her greatest source of joy and inspiration.

She is an Elementary Art Teacher and enjoys camping, swimming, dark chocolate and movie nights with her family. In her spare time she can be found painting, sewing, writing or illustrating children's books. She is an eternal optimist and wishes that everyone could see the world as she does with all of its beauty, hope and goodness. She hopes to inspire others to have joy and use their imaginations through her books.

For more information please contact Inspire Joy Publishing, LLC at. https://www.facebook.com/MelanieHawkinsAuthor/
Email: MelanieHawkinsAuthor@gmail.com
IG: Instagram.com/melaniehawkinsauthor
Look for the Little Bug series and more inspiring books to come by this same author & illustrator

Made in United States
North Haven, CT
13 March 2022